This bite-sized book has been designed to give you a useful overview of relaxation and help you to achieve the following:

- Understand the value of building time into your day for relaxation
- Learn about the benefits of taking time to relax
- Discover ways to recharge and boost your energy
- Find ways to switch off and calm your mind chatter
- Improve your physical and mental health
- Manage stress and avoid burnout

GW00658696

Take a rest; a field that has rested gives a bountiful crop

Ovid

# Modern life

We are living in the busy ages and modern life seems to be so much about rushing around, trying to keep lots of balls in the air. It is so important to bear in mind that for all the time you are on output you need to balance this with rest and relaxation so that you can recover and recharge.

Building relaxation time into your life will help you to keep your stress levels down and look after your overall well-being. Too much work and not enough time out for yourself can result in physical and mental health problems. Winding down and relaxing is essential if you want to invest in achieving better balance and living a happier and healthier life.

Burnout is what happens
when you try to avoid being
human for too long

Michael Gungor

# Stress and burnout

In a world where we seem to be constantly switched on and overwhelmed, it can be challenging to establish a healthy life balance. Everyday pressures can build up and affect your stress levels without you even being aware that it is happening. The creep of burnout is insidious.

According to the World Health Organization, burnout is the 21st-century health epidemic and is a state of emotional, physical and mental exhaustion that is caused by excessive and prolonged stress. It occurs when people feel overwhelmed, emotionally drained, and unable to meet pressures and demands. Burnout can affect anyone and building relaxation into your everyday life is essential to combat this.

## Some of the benefits of relaxation

- Lowers your blood pressure
- Slows your breathing rate
- Slows your heart rate down
- Reduces activity of stress hormones
- Increases blood flow to major muscles
- Reduces muscle tension and chronic pain
- Improves concentration and mood
- Maintains normal blood sugar levels
- Improves your digestion
- Boosts your energy levels
- Supports your mental health
- Helps you to be present and appreciate the moment

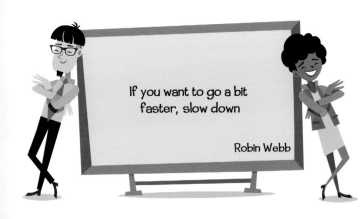

If you want to go a bit
faster, slow down

Robin Webb

## Slow down and smell the roses

There is more to life than rushing around like busy fools and not necessarily being productive. The founder of the Roman Empire *Augustus* would use the Latin phrase *Festina Lente* which translates into *Make haste, slowly*. This served as a reminder for Augustus and his army to perform activities with a proper balance of urgency and diligence.

By focusing on the moment and appreciating the experience rather than being somewhere else will heighten your enjoyment of whatever activity you are involved in. Tapping into and focusing on all your senses will help you to appreciate much more of what is going on around you, which in turn, can have a very relaxing effect. Being around nature and green spaces can also be energising and lift your mood, which will ultimately help you to be more productive.

Sleep is the golden chain that
ties health and our bodies together

Thomas Dekker

## Relaxation and sleep

Sleep can so often be an overlooked and neglected component of overall health and well-being. It is so important because it enables your body to repair and be fit for the day ahead. Various studies suggest that getting adequate sleep may also help prevent excess weight gain, heart disease and increased illness during times of stress.

If you are challenged with sleepless nights you will know how it feels to have your mind buzzing with anxiety while you are desperately tossing and turning with frustration. Relaxation can help you switch off and promote much better quality of sleep, which, in turn, will help you to recharge your batteries and cope better generally.

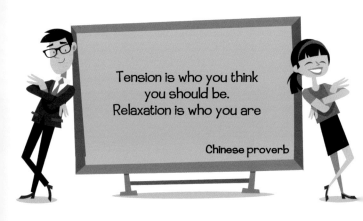

Tension is who you think
you should be.
Relaxation is who you are

Chinese proverb

# How
# to relax

## Set time aside to relax

Setting aside time for yourself within your busy schedule is all about self-care and establishing healthy boundaries. Making your own personal well-being your biggest priority has nothing to do with being selfish and no one needs to feel guilty about this. It is the most responsible approach to living a healthy and productive life.

When you plan your day it is important to allocate time for relaxation and put this on your to-do list. Getting outside at lunchtime for a relaxing stroll or even just taking a few minutes to do some stretching and breathing exercises can make all the difference. If you don't set the time aside however, you may not get around to doing it, so it pays to be organised and disciplined about this.

# Switch off

It is becoming increasingly obvious that our world is developing an unhealthy attachment to technology and mobile devices. Being able to switch off from technology will help you to relax quite significantly.

Various studies into neurological and emotional well-being highlight the need to take breaks. Scanning social media is not a break for your brain because your mind will think it is still working. When you relax you really need to switch off and avoid directing your thoughts toward any task at all. Downtime is healthy for the mind and body.

Almost everything will work again if you unplug it for a while, including you!

My goal is no longer to get more done, but rather to have less to do

Francine Jay

# Lighten your load

Take a good look at your life and work out what is really important. It can be so easy to accumulate stuff and overcomplicate your life if you are not careful. This will not help you to feel relaxed. There is real beauty in keeping things as simple as possible and avoiding stuffocation!

Decluttering and being tidy will help you to feel far more organised and calm. It can be stressful trying to find things in a cluttered environment. Every now and then it can be very therapeutic and cleansing to have a sort and work out what you don't really need any more.

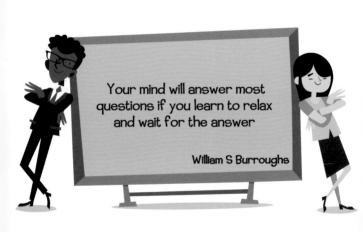

Your mind will answer most
questions if you learn to relax
and wait for the answer

William S Burroughs

# Manage your mind chatter

We literally have tens of thousands of thoughts a day and the quality of those thoughts will have a big impact on how relaxed you feel. Negative mind chatter can be exhausting, especially if you are worried about something and it is playing on your mind. Reframing your thoughts can be really helpful in calming negative thinking.

Here are five questions to help you reframe your negative thoughts:

1. What else could this mean?
2. Am I jumping to negative conclusions?
3. What is the best part about this situation or person?
4. Am I filtering out the positives and dwelling on the negatives?
5. What are the benefits of these thoughts to me?

# Be mindful

The term mindfulness comes from Eastern spiritual and religious traditions. It is a very old concept and is a key part of Buddhism, and also appears in Hindu writings.

A great deal of scientific research now shows that the mindful approach to stress, anxiety and mental health is a very helpful and popular way of dealing with and diffusing high levels of stress.

Mindfulness refers to being completely in touch with and aware of the present moment, as well as taking a non-evaluative and non-judgmental approach to your inner experience. It is essentially about being present and noticing what is around you. So often, if you are not careful, you can find yourself racing through life in a mad dash and not taking time to stop and really appreciate what is happening in your life.

# Practise meditation

Meditation is the habitual process of training your mind to focus and redirect your thoughts. It combines focused breathing whilst paying attention to what is happening in the present moment. There are lots of different ways to meditate so it is always useful to test out a few and see what works best for you. Some people find that using a mantra helps them stay calm and focused. Simply repeating a word or phrase over and over again as you relax and breathe slowly can be highly effective.

Some meditation practitioners may suggest visualisation and creating a calm, idyllic image in your mind. So close your eyes and paint a picture in your mind of a calming place and fill it in with sensory information. Ask yourself the following questions - what does it look like? Sound like? Smell like?

# Practise Yoga

The literal meaning of the Sanskrit word yoga is 'yoke'. Yoga is defined as a means of uniting the individual spirit with the universal spirit. Yoga is a form of exercise that evolved from ancient India thousands of years ago. The main components of yoga are postures and a series of movements that are designed to increase strength, flexibility and breathing.

Studies suggest that yoga, under professional supervision, is a safe and effective way to increase physical activity. There is also evidence that regular yoga practice is beneficial for people with high blood pressure, heart disease, aches and pains, depression and stress.

# Focus on breathing

Breathing has to be the easiest form of relaxation and when you focus on breathing it can really help you to calm down if you are feeling stressed. There are many simple breathing exercises that are very easy and require no equipment and can be done anywhere.

Here is one example:

- Sit with your back straight and imagine a piece of string attached to the top of your head pulling you up.
- Close your eyes and focus on your breathing.
- Place the tip of your tongue behind your upper front teeth.
- Close your mouth and inhale through your nose to a mental count of four.
- Hold your breath for a count of four.
- Exhale completely through your mouth, slowly, to a count of eight.
- This is one breath. Now repeat.

# Use essential oils

Diffusers can be really helpful with relaxation and disperse essential oils as a fine vapour through the air so they can be absorbed gently into the body through your respiratory system. The smells from the essential oils can also encourage the nervous system to transmit signals to the limbic system in the brain which handles emotion.

Some of the best essential oils for relaxation include:

- Lavender
- Rose
- Ylang-ylang
- Bergamot
- Chamomile
- Jasmine
- Clary sage
- Cedarwood

## Sip something soothing

Herbal teas can help you to relax and can provide a mix of calming ingredients. For example, teas containing lavender, valerian, passion flower and chamomile soothe and calm the nervous system.

Sipping something soothing can also give you an opportunity to slow down and relish the present moment. The whole ritual of making a cup of tea then sitting down to sip the tea, peacefully, is a form of relaxation in itself. Lovely!

# Stroke a pet

Spending time around pets can help you to relax and feel calmer. When you stroke an animal you release feel-good endorphins that help to reduce your heart rate.

Playing with a pet also increases the levels of the feel-good chemicals serotonin and dopamine in your brain, which can help you feel happier.

There are many benefits to being around animals and even if you don't have your own pet you can always offer to look after someone else's from time to time.

# Play relaxing music

Music is also a great way of helping you to relax, relieve stress and ease any anxieties you may have. It can also help you to function better mentally and physically.

Music is regularly used for meditation and as an aid for sleep disorders. Some studies have suggested that slow, gentle, soothing music can also improve learning, creativity and memory.

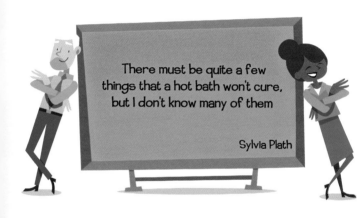

There must be quite a few
things that a hot bath won't cure,
but I don't know many of them

Sylvia Plath

# Soak in the bath

One simple method that you can build into the fabric of your day is a warm bath. Warm water and a bubble bath will loosen up your muscles and it's a great way to feel pampered without really doing a lot.

It will also deepen respiration and take any tension away from your body, which will push all the stresses and strains of the day straight down the plughole! Fifteen minutes soaking in a warm, scented bath will help you feel relaxed and lighten your mind. Candles and calming music can be an additional way to luxuriate.

# Light a candle

Candles can be very soothing and their light makes them a perfect aid for relaxation. By focusing on the candle flame it will increase awareness and calm an anxious mind. For additional benefits, scented candles can be used which create a more broad-reaching sensory experience.

For a safe, healthy and tranquil atmosphere choose soy candles infused with natural essential oils. These are more environmentally friendly because they are renewable, free of toxins and biodegradable.

# Doodle

There are numerous reasons why doodling is good to help you relax. The repetition and rhythmic motions of sketching can activate the relaxation response as a way of combating stress. Colouring books have also been proven to calm the amygdala, the part of the brain that controls your stress response.

While journaling is a great way to get in touch with your thoughts and feelings, you can get even better results if you add doodles to your journal entries. It's amazing how therapeutic it can be.

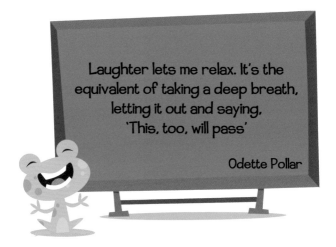

Laughter lets me relax. It's the equivalent of taking a deep breath, letting it out and saying, 'This, too, will pass'

Odette Pollar

# Let the laughter in

Having a good laugh can decrease stress hormones and also increase immune cells and infection-fighting antibodies. Laughter has so many benefits and can be such a great tonic, as well as helping you to relax. Even in challenging times it helps to seek out the funny side of situations.

Laughter also triggers the release of endorphins, the body's natural feel-good chemicals. Endorphins promote an overall sense of well-being and can even temporarily relieve pain, as well as having a very positive effect on your emotional well-being.

Many people are alive but
don't touch the miracle
of being alive

Thich Nhat Hanh

## Explore more relaxation

The following websites have been a very useful resource for researching and compiling this bite-sized book. Here is a wealth of information to explore.

- www.thriveglobal.com
- www.calm.com
- www.oxfordmindfulness.org
- www.headspace.com
- www.buddhify.com
- www.mind.org.uk
- www.actionforhappiness.org
- www.verywellmind.com
- www.selfgrowth.com/relaxation

How beautiful it is to do nothing,
and then to rest afterwards

Spanish proverb